Color to Declutter:

A thoughtful collection of unique designs that will help bring your inner and outer worlds into alignment.

Illustrations and text by	Jean Prominski
Edited by	Erica Rodgers & Keith Creighton
Cover art and layout by	Steve Ruttner
Published by	Seattle Sparkle

Images from Dr. Emoto used with permission from Office Masaru Emoto, LLC.

Welcome to *Color to Declutter: A thoughtful collection of unique designs that will help bring your inner and outer worlds into alignment.*

Before we get too deep into an ocean of reasons why coloring is as great for adults as it is for kids–let's not forget the biggest reason of all. It's fun! And compared to the prices of other forms of entertainment–it's cheap! Oh I could go on and on…so I will!

Beyond delivering pure unbridled joy, the process of coloring is one of the best ways to get organized and stay organized. If done with intention, you can color your way to an organized home and uncluttered mind. Ok, there may be a few more steps involved, but once you start coloring, you'll see!

Each design in the pages that follow awaits your pen and pencils. As you color, you'll also develop your planning and strategizing skills. Included on each page is an **essence word** that represents the design. Think about and feel the meaning of the word while you bring your personal rainbow to each letter and water crystal. Getting in touch with your emotional and sensory awareness of these words will help you understand your connections to the objects or ideas you want to organize in your life. As you color, you can repeat the word in your head until you can feel it in your body. Knowing how you honestly feel about the things you surround yourself with is a very important part of the organizing process.

Coloring brings confidence to the decision making process. One of the many reasons why I chose water crystals (or "snowflakes") to be the theme of this book is their color in the natural world. At a distance, water crystals appear to be white. Shine a light on them, and you'll see a prism of color. How you color the pages that follow is solely up to you- there are no rules, except follow your muse.

As you make decisions while coloring, you will notice how your confidence is mirrored while organizing in everyday life. For example, the process of deciding which page to color first, whether it is the easiest or the most fun, can be a way to approach a garage cleaning project. If you decide to start with the section of the garage that you'll enjoy doing the most, this might help you track your progress better and keep your momentum going. For the following decision, choosing the colors you want in your design will echo real life decisions, like making choices about where you want to store your items in the garage.

Now that you've picked a water crystal, where do you begin? Do you start by coloring the center of the design or begin with an outer portion? Do you finish coloring similar elements before moving on to the next? Or do you color from left to right? Do you use a color pattern or make every crystal unique? In the physical world, how would you start the garage clean out? Do you gather all of the woodworking tools that are scattered in various nooks and crannies and put them together, or do you work from one side of the garage to the other? If you have already decided to tackle the easiest part of the garage, then how do you start to organize? Do you start by tossing out all the garbage? Your choices on

Aligned

how you want to color will help you expose your decision making process, which is easily transferable to just about anything.

One of the biggest challenges in both coloring and staying organized is keeping your motivation up when you hit a snag- like when you accidentally grab and use the pink pencil when your heart wanted orange. Or when you can't decide what to do with a box of vases you have had for a decade. Do you shrug your shoulders and try a different angle? Do you take a short break and come back with new found excitement? Coloring this book can help reveal your individual motivation process.

Last, but not least, how do you feel once you have completed the coloring page, or alternatively, the garage organization? Are you proud of yourself, impressed, and amazed? Do you share the excitement with your friends and family? Use this coloring book as a stepping stone to better understand your organization techniques.

Why We Color

Coloring harmonizes the mind. Creating artwork, such as adding color to paper (both inside and outside the lines) improves blood flow to the prefrontal cortex, which is the part of your brain that promotes creative thinking, decision making and planning. Acknowledge the positive observations you make about yourself and your home when you engage in regular intervals of coloring. Increasing the capacity of your prefrontal cortex will also aid your memory. That way you can remember where you have placed items in your home, like keys, scissors, or a document you only need on rare occasions. Organizing your home will become easier based on the fact that you are essentially rewiring your brain to a more harmonized state.

Coloring also soothes the amygdala, the almond-sized cluster in our brain that controls the fight or flight response. If you watch the news or check your email "one more time" before bed, you're likely to trigger your amygdala and set worry or fear into motion. Coloring is a quiet, contained and controlled entertainment; the biggest risk you take is an ink pen leaking or a pencil tip breaking, As you choose what colors go where, when and why, you will put the creative (right) side of your brain into alignment with the logical (left) side. You create a world exactly as you want it, without any jarring "Breaking News" graphics to interrupt your flow.

Coloring is rewarding. As if the aforementioned benefits weren't enough, the prefrontal cortex is the brain's reward center. Studies have shown how the pleasure and process of creating art delivers a "reward" to the brain in the form of pride, accomplishment, and entertainment. By rewarding yourself by creating art, you're less likely to seek rewards by doing things that are not in your best interest, including unnecessary or excessive snacking, drinking, shopping, or screen time.

Coloring delivers internal balance. Your mind and body are fully engaged when you are coloring. Your brain is making decisions and discerning the information received from your senses, such as, determining which colors go where and observing your work to see if it looks good or not. Conversely, your body is touching the paper, smelling the freshly sharpened pencils, or ink from a pen. All of this engagement helps awaken and balance your soul. If your soul is balanced, your life is balanced. Another word for balanced is "organized".

Coloring strengthens your boundaries and identity. The act of choosing colors, expressing preferences, and doing what you want (rather than doing what other people tell you to do) builds courage, self-esteem, and self-expression. It helps you to better understand YOUR state of flow. This is mirrored in the home organizing process when you give yourself permission to use the space in the way that supports your own unique way of living. Your preferences may be shown in the layout of furniture, the activities you make space for, and the colors, textures or themes you choose. If you have an unused guest room and also suffer from lack of closet space in the master bedroom- create a walk-in closet and turn the least-used room in the house into the most-used one.

No longer will you have to designate space for creating a facade for what others prefer, or making room for activities that you don't really want to participate in. You can let your space fall into alignment with your goals and priorities. Instead of people-pleasing or overextending yourself to gain approval, your newly strengthened sense of self will ensure that you can conserve your energy to spend it in ways that enhance your wellbeing. Let coloring help you live in your home instead of someone else's.

Coloring promotes self-contentment. The repetition of patterns can promote a sense of calm based on predictability. Built up over time, personal accomplishments will give you the confidence to know that you can finish what you set out to do!

Contentment builds credibility and self-respect. The repetition of coloring can flip your mind from ruminating on negative thoughts to ruminating on coordinated self-contented thoughts. Your brain will naturally prefer to repeat this organized thinking in your home. Your default preference (conscious or subconscious) may have been to choose to have stacks of paper to sort, trash to take out, or cluttered and stagnant display shelves to "deal with". Coloring with focus will allow your brain to constantly organize instead of letting messes accumulate. Your new default preferences may include automatic sorting, choosing and recycling based upon the repetition of pattern, predictability, and purpose. The cherry on this sundae is the constant dopamine hit of accomplishment.

Coloring is relaxing. Spending quiet time, away from screens, promotes a sense of self -attunement. Without the brightness of a screen, or the stimulation delivered by some of its content, you'll have better sleep. Better sleep equals better health and more brainpower to make healthy and self synchronizing decisions. By being tuning into yourself, without social media or TV as a distraction, you will develop a greater patience for yourself and others. Cultivating a sense of self-attunement means that you are aware of the signals your body is telling you, and your actions align with your goals and values. As your ability to turn inward increases, your home will reflect this as well. No longer will you need to fill a sense of emptiness or loneliness with retail therapy or overindulging in other ways that may result in clutter or a cycle of shame and guilt. Coloring helps quiet the distractions of the world and reveal your true passions and desires.

The Magic of Water Crystals

Your inner world creates your outer world and your outer world creates your inner world. Dr. Masaru Emoto experiments with this theory in his book, **"The Hidden Messages of Water"**. In his studies with ice crystal formations, Dr. Emoto would expose containers of water to different sounds, pictures or words (verbal or thoughts). He showed water that was entrained with words like "peace", "gratitude", and "love" all formed intricate and symmetrical structural formations. When he used words representing hate and anger, the crystal formations would be off balance, malformed or broken. Like the concepts Emoto poses, the words, thoughts, memories, images and noises in your environment will undoubtedly have an effect on your internal structure.

How does this relate to you? Think about the objects in your home as words. What words are they? Are they loving, kind and compassionate? Or are they the type of words that create structural disharmony? Letting go of items that don't support your internal snowflake may even rewire your memories of the past!

While the destabilizing energy of structural disharmony is required in some situations, a continual stream of negative energy is unsustainable and can create chaos. Choose to welcome in the energy that promotes stability. Once you learn the lesson disequilibrium can teach you, you will feel grounded, safe and sure.

When the objects and images in our environment light us up and align with our goals and values, they create a positive ripple effect. These water crystal designs are positive representations of the things you can choose to fill your home. The benefits of coloring will help you declutter and organize your space. You will become more insightful about your relationships, career, time, diet, and much more.

Two of Dr. Emoto's Water Crystals

"You Are Beautiful"

"Thank You"

Yes—You are a Snowflake...

...and that is NOT an insult. Since a large percentage of your body is made up of water, what types of crystals would form inside of you if you were frozen? A snowflake is intricate, symmetrical and balanced, so, what does your internal snowflake look like? What do you need to shift in your home or life to be a stunning and well-formed snowflake? It is easy to only recognize the imperfections of our home and life, but notice the beauty in "imperfection". The universe makes no mistakes. Trust that everything is happening with perfect timing. Each crystal formation is different, just as no one person is the same, so color your way to find your strategy to get organized.

Love

Peace

Groovy

Gratitude

Harmony

Delight

Joy

Centered

Kindness

Radiant

Balance

Cheer

Happy

Bright

Twinkle

Paradise

Fertile

Good

Compassion

Calm

Grounded

Pleased

Shine

Sweet

Valuable

Glimmer

Superb

Wonderful

Aligned

Splendid

Super Bueno

Marvelous

Special

Bliss

Smile

Glow

Brilliant

Abundance

Smart

Warm

Incandesce

Enchanted

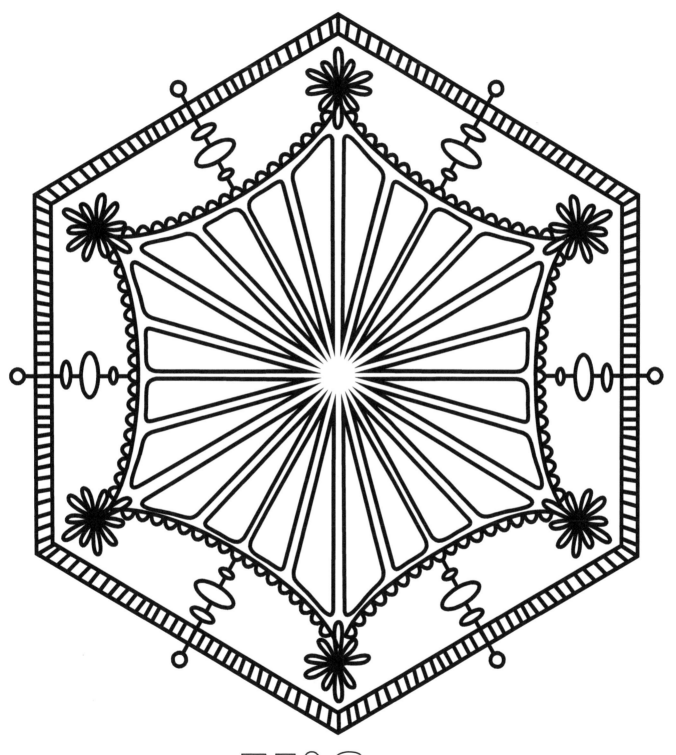

Nifty

Effervesce

Powerful

Well

Breathe

Worthy

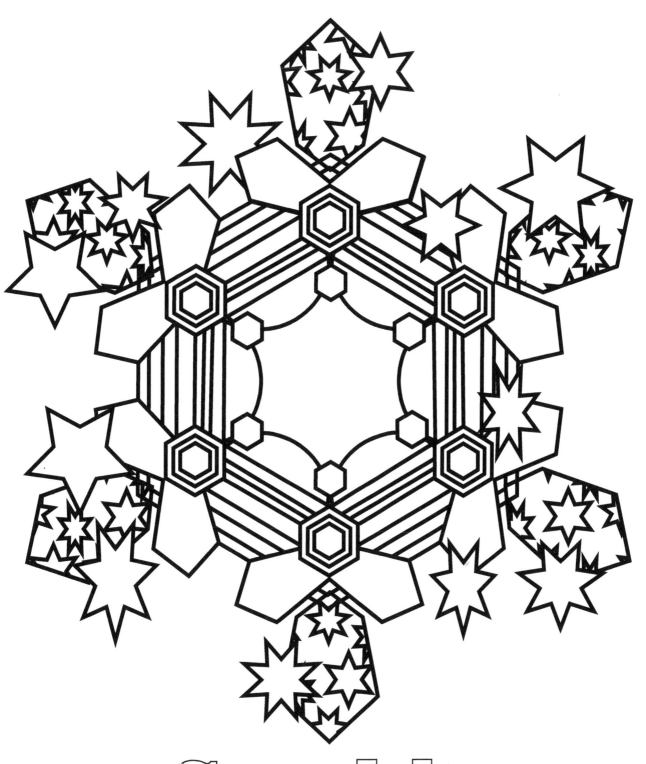

Sparkle

The Kerfuffle...

The last design is dedicated to:
My cousin Gillian, who is particular about what she likes to color.
and
People who need something to say to blow off some steam.
For instance, anyone who has ever walked a Parson "Jack" Russell Terrier like mine. #terrierlife

I own a Jack Russell Terrier, Maisy, and learn a lot from her every day.
According to Jack Russells, "kerfuffle" is a word that can simultaneously mean both "naughty and nice", "conflict and snuggles", "friend and enemy", "fluffy and spiky", "making a mess and being really cute". It can be used as an adjective, a verb and a noun. Kerfuffle is the ultimate paradox. The "Jack Russell Kerfuffle" is an event to be experienced. If you ever need to just "cool off" or otherwise don't know what to say, asking yourself "What the kerfuffle?" is sure to bring your snowflake back into alignment.

PHOTO: Shannon Garbaccio Photography

CPSIA information can be obtained
at www.ICGtesting.com
Printed in the USA
BVHW092338090220
571891BV00001B/2